THE
CHRISTIAN
NOTETAKER'S
JOURNAL

A Treasury of Personal Growth & Ministry

THE CHRISTIAN NOTETAKER'S JOURNAL

Unless otherwise noted, Scripture quotations are from
The Holy Bible, King James Version.

ISBN: 0-8499-5165-8 Burgundy

Printed in Belgium

Presented to

Dad

From

Barbara

Date

12-25-95

Occasion

Christmas

INTRODUCTION

How many times have you found yourself in a church service or other inspirational setting and you wanted to take notes, but you had nothing to write on. So you find a scrap of paper, a bulletin, an offering envelope, the margin of your Bible or anything else that will do for the moment to take notes on.

Then what happens to your notes? You tuck them away in your pocket or Bible, lose them, throw them away or simply never look at them again. Even if you ever do refer to them, the "unofficial" way you scribbled them down in the the first place somehow doesn't inspire much confidence as you re-read them now.

The Christian NoteTaker's Journal is designed to solve this problem. It's purpose is to help you document the special thoughts, insights, names, resources, etc., in a simple and orderly manner and preserve them forever. It will represent the best of what you have gleaned from a variety of sources over a period of time.

Our desire is that *The Christian NoteTaker's Journal* will become your spiritual companion and, hopefully, a valued treasure to which you will refer often for inspiration and blessing.

CONTENTS

How To Use
THE CHRISTIAN NOTETAKER'S JOURNAL

NOTES

This portion of the Journal is for taking notes at worship services, Bible studies, conventions, conferences, retreats, banquets and at a variety of other special events. Be sure to fill in the information at the top of each page of notes.

SCRIPTURE REFERENCE LOG

As soon as possible after taking notes, transfer to the "Scripture Reference Log" the information asked for. This will provide an orderly review of material you have studied – arranged according to books of the Bible – for easy referencing.

HUMOR & ILLUSTRATIONS

Use this section to write down humorous stories, quotes and illustrations.

MUSIC

Make notes of songs, composers, soloists, musical groups, etc., for future reference.

BOOKS & TAPES

Recommended book titles, tapes and other resources should be recorded in this section.

PRAYER LIST

Cultivate the habit of praying regularly for individuals and situations included on your prayer list.

SCRIPTURE MEMORY SCHEDULE

Included in this section are 52 favorite Bible verses – one for each week of the year – that you will enjoy committing to memory. You will want to check them off as you memorize them. Also, here are four tips that make memorization easier.
1. Try to understand the thought and meaning of the verse.
2. Memorize "out loud." Speak the verse over and over out loud, so your voice, hearing and mind all participate simultaneously in the memorization process.
3. Concentrate!
4. Review memorized verses out loud until they are firmly embedded in your heart and mind. Then they are yours.

THROUGH-THE-BIBLE-IN-A-YEAR READING SCHEDULE

This is a delightful daily Bible reading plan for reading the entire Bible through in one year. The program suggests reading completely through a book before moving on to another book, and then alternating Old and New Testament books for balance and variety.

CONFERENCES, MEETINGS & SPECIAL EVENTS

When you hear the announcement of some future conference, concert or other special event, jot it down in this section.

NAMES & ADDRESSES

Write down contacts, names, etc., of people you meet on various occasions.

CRISIS SCRIPTURE GUIDE

You will find this section to be inspirational and helpful both to you and to those to whom you minister, particularly in times of crisis.

NOTES

NOTES

Speaker *Pastor John Bell*   Date _____

Topic/Title _____ Place/Event _____

Reference/Text _____

_____

_____

_____

_____

_____

_____

_____

_____

_____

_____

_____

_____

_____

_____

_____

_____

_____

_____

_____

_____

_____

_____

_____

_____

_____

_____

_____

_____

NOTES

Speaker _____ *Date* _____

Topic/Title _____ *Place/Event* _____

Reference/Text _____

_____

_____

_____

_____

_____

_____

_____

_____

_____

_____

_____

_____

_____

_____

_____

_____

_____

_____

_____

_____

_____

_____

_____

_____

_____

_____

_____

_____

_____

NOTES

Speaker _____ *Date* _____

Topic/Title _____ *Place/Event* _____

Reference/Text _____

_____

_____

_____

_____

_____

_____

_____

_____

_____

_____

_____

_____

_____

_____

_____

_____

_____

_____

_____

_____

_____

_____

_____

_____

_____

_____

_____

NOTES

Speaker _____ *Date* _____

Topic/Title _____ *Place/Event* _____

Reference/Text _____

_____

_____

_____

_____

_____

_____

_____

_____

_____

_____

_____

_____

_____

_____

_____

_____

_____

_____

_____

_____

_____

_____

_____

_____

_____

_____

_____

_____

NOTES

Speaker _____ *Date* _____

Topic/Title _____ *Place/Event* _____

Reference/Text _____

_____

_____

_____

_____

_____

_____

_____

_____

_____

_____

_____

_____

_____

_____

_____

_____

_____

_____

_____

_____

_____

_____

_____

_____

_____

_____

_____

_____

_____

_____

NOTES

Speaker _____ *Date* _____

Topic/Title _____ *Place/Event* _____

Reference/Text _____

_____

_____

_____

_____

_____

_____

_____

_____

_____

_____

_____

_____

_____

_____

_____

_____

_____

_____

_____

_____

_____

_____

_____

_____

_____

_____

_____

_____

_____

NOTES

Speaker _____ *Date* _____

Topic/Title _____ *Place/Event* _____

Reference/Text _____

_____

_____

_____

_____

_____

_____

_____

_____

_____

_____

_____

_____

_____

_____

_____

_____

_____

_____

_____

_____

_____

_____

_____

_____

_____

_____

_____

NOTES

Speaker _____ *Date* _____

Topic/Title _____ *Place/Event* _____

Reference/Text _____

_____

_____

_____

_____

_____

_____

_____

_____

_____

_____

_____

_____

_____

_____

_____

_____

_____

_____

_____

_____

_____

_____

_____

_____

_____

_____

_____

_____

_____

NOTES

Speaker _____ *Date* _____

Topic/Title _____ *Place/Event* _____

Reference/Text _____

_____

_____

_____

_____

_____

_____

_____

_____

_____

_____

_____

_____

_____

_____

_____

_____

_____

_____

_____

_____

_____

_____

_____

_____

_____

NOTES

Speaker _____ *Date* _____

Topic/Title _____ *Place/Event* _____

Reference/Text _____

NOTES

Speaker _____ *Date* _____

Topic/Title _____ *Place/Event* _____

Reference/Text _____

_____

_____

_____

_____

_____

_____

_____

_____

_____

_____

_____

_____

_____

_____

_____

_____

_____

_____

_____

_____

_____

_____

_____

_____

_____

_____

_____

_____

_____

NOTES

Speaker _____ *Date* _____

Topic/Title _____ *Place/Event* _____

Reference/Text _____

_____

_____

_____

_____

_____

_____

_____

_____

_____

_____

_____

_____

_____

_____

_____

_____

_____

_____

_____

_____

_____

_____

_____

_____

_____

_____

_____

_____

_____

_____

NOTES

Speaker _____ Date _____

Topic/Title _____ Place/Event _____

Reference/Text _____

_____

_____

_____

_____

_____

_____

_____

_____

_____

_____

_____

_____

_____

_____

_____

_____

_____

_____

_____

_____

_____

_____

_____

_____

_____

_____

_____

_____

NOTES

Speaker _____ *Date* _____

Topic/Title _____ *Place/Event* _____

Reference/Text _____

_____

_____

_____

_____

_____

_____

_____

_____

_____

_____

_____

_____

_____

_____

_____

_____

_____

_____

_____

_____

_____

_____

_____

_____

_____

_____

_____

_____

_____

_____

_____

NOTES

Speaker _____ *Date* _____

Topic/Title _____ *Place/Event* _____

Reference/Text _____

_____

_____

_____

_____

_____

_____

_____

_____

_____

_____

_____

_____

_____

_____

_____

_____

_____

_____

_____

_____

_____

_____

_____

_____

_____

NOTES

Speaker _____ Date _____

Topic/Title _____ Place/Event _____

Reference/Text _____

_____

_____

_____

_____

_____

_____

_____

_____

_____

_____

_____

_____

_____

_____

_____

_____

_____

_____

_____

_____

_____

_____

_____

_____

_____

_____

_____

_____

_____

_____

NOTES

Speaker _____ *Date* _____

Topic/Title _____ *Place/Event* _____

Reference/Text _____

_____

_____

_____

_____

_____

_____

_____

_____

_____

_____

_____

_____

_____

_____

_____

_____

_____

_____

_____

_____

_____

_____

_____

_____

_____

_____

_____

_____

NOTES

Speaker _____ *Date* _____

Topic/Title _____ *Place/Event* _____

Reference/Text _____

_____

_____

_____

_____

_____

_____

_____

_____

_____

_____

_____

_____

_____

_____

_____

_____

_____

_____

_____

_____

_____

_____

_____

_____

_____

_____

_____

_____

NOTES

Speaker _____ *Date* _____

Topic/Title _____ *Place/Event* _____

Reference/Text _____

_____

_____

_____

_____

_____

_____

_____

_____

_____

_____

_____

_____

_____

_____

_____

_____

_____

_____

_____

_____

_____

_____

_____

_____

_____

_____

_____

_____

_____

NOTES

Speaker _____ *Date* _____

Topic/Title _____ *Place/Event* _____

Reference/Text _____

_____

_____

_____

_____

_____

_____

_____

_____

_____

_____

_____

_____

_____

_____

_____

_____

_____

_____

_____

_____

_____

_____

_____

_____

NOTES

Speaker _____ *Date* _____

Topic/Title _____ *Place/Event* _____

Reference/Text _____

_____

_____

_____

_____

_____

_____

_____

_____

_____

_____

_____

_____

_____

_____

_____

_____

_____

_____

_____

_____

_____

_____

_____

_____

_____

_____

NOTES

Speaker _____ *Date* _____

Topic/Title _____ *Place/Event* _____

Reference/Text _____

_____

_____

_____

_____

_____

_____

_____

_____

_____

_____

_____

_____

_____

_____

_____

_____

_____

_____

_____

_____

_____

_____

_____

_____

_____

_____

_____

_____

NOTES

Speaker _____ *Date* _____

Topic/Title _____ *Place/Event* _____

Reference/Text _____

_____

_____

_____

_____

_____

_____

_____

_____

_____

_____

_____

_____

_____

_____

_____

_____

_____

_____

_____

_____

_____

_____

_____

_____

_____

_____

_____

_____

_____

NOTES

Speaker _____ *Date* _____

Topic/Title _____ *Place/Event* _____

Reference/Text _____

_____

_____

_____

_____

_____

_____

_____

_____

_____

_____

_____

_____

_____

_____

_____

_____

_____

_____

_____

_____

_____

_____

_____

_____

_____

_____

_____

NOTES

Speaker _____ *Date* _____

Topic/Title _____ *Place/Event* _____

Reference/Text _____

_____

_____

_____

_____

_____

_____

_____

_____

_____

_____

_____

_____

_____

_____

_____

_____

_____

_____

_____

_____

_____

_____

_____

_____

_____

_____

_____

NOTES

Speaker _____ *Date* _____

Topic/Title _____ *Place/Event* _____

Reference/Text _____

NOTES

Speaker _____ *Date* _____

Topic/Title _____ *Place/Event* _____

Reference/Text _____

_____

_____

_____

_____

_____

_____

_____

_____

_____

_____

_____

_____

_____

_____

_____

_____

_____

_____

_____

_____

_____

_____

_____

_____

_____

_____

_____

NOTES

Speaker _____ *Date* _____

Topic/Title _____ *Place/Event* _____

Reference/Text _____

_____

_____

_____

_____

_____

_____

_____

_____

_____

_____

_____

_____

_____

_____

_____

_____

_____

_____

_____

_____

_____

_____

_____

_____

_____

_____

_____

_____

_____

_____

_____

NOTES

Speaker _____ *Date* _____

Topic/Title _____ *Place/Event* _____

Reference/Text _____

_____

_____

_____

_____

_____

_____

_____

_____

_____

_____

_____

_____

_____

_____

_____

_____

_____

_____

_____

_____

_____

_____

_____

_____

_____

_____

NOTES

Speaker _____ *Date* _____

Topic/Title _____ *Place/Event* _____

Reference/Text _____

_____

_____

_____

_____

_____

_____

_____

_____

_____

_____

_____

_____

_____

_____

_____

_____

_____

_____

_____

_____

_____

_____

_____

_____

_____

_____

NOTES

Speaker _____ Date _____

Topic/Title _____ Place/Event _____

Reference/Text _____

_____

_____

_____

_____

_____

_____

_____

_____

_____

_____

_____

_____

_____

_____

_____

_____

_____

_____

_____

_____

_____

_____

_____

_____

_____

_____

Notes

Speaker _____ *Date* _____

Topic/Title _____ *Place/Event* _____

Reference/Text _____

_____

_____

_____

_____

_____

_____

_____

_____

_____

_____

_____

_____

_____

_____

_____

_____

_____

_____

_____

_____

_____

_____

_____

_____

_____

_____

_____

NOTES

Speaker _____ *Date* _____

Topic/Title _____ *Place/Event* _____

Reference/Text _____

_____

_____

_____

_____

_____

_____

_____

_____

_____

_____

_____

_____

_____

_____

_____

_____

_____

_____

_____

_____

_____

_____

_____

_____

_____

_____

_____

_____

NOTES

Speaker _____ Date _____

Topic/Title _____ Place/Event _____

Reference/Text _____

_____ _____

_____

_____

_____

_____

_____

_____

_____

_____

_____

_____

_____

_____

_____

_____

_____

_____

_____

_____

_____

_____

_____

_____

_____

_____

_____

_____

_____

NOTES

Speaker _____ *Date* _____

Topic/Title _____ *Place/Event* _____

Reference/Text _____

_____

_____

_____

_____

_____

_____

_____

_____

_____

_____

_____

_____

_____

_____

_____

_____

_____

_____

_____

_____

_____

_____

_____

_____

_____

_____

_____

_____

NOTES

Speaker _____ *Date* _____

Topic/Title _____ *Place/Event* _____

Reference/Text _____

_____ _____

_____

_____

_____

_____

_____

_____

_____

_____

_____

_____

_____

_____

_____

_____

_____

_____

_____

_____

_____

_____

_____

_____

_____

_____

_____

_____

_____

_____

_____

NOTES

Speaker _____ Date _____

Topic/Title _____ Place/Event _____

Reference/Text _____

_____

_____

_____

_____

_____

_____

_____

_____

_____

_____

_____

_____

_____

_____

_____

_____

_____

_____

_____

_____

_____

_____

_____

_____

_____

_____

_____

_____

_____

NOTES

Speaker _____ *Date* _____

Topic/Title _____ *Place/Event* _____

Reference/Text _____

NOTES

Speaker _____ *Date* _____

Topic/Title _____ *Place/Event* _____

Reference/Text _____

_____

_____

_____

_____

_____

_____

_____

_____

_____

_____

_____

_____

_____

_____

_____

_____

_____

_____

_____

_____

_____

_____

_____

_____

_____

_____

NOTES

Speaker _____ *Date* _____

Topic/Title _____ *Place/Event* _____

Reference/Text _____

_____

_____

_____

_____

_____

_____

_____

_____

_____

_____

_____

_____

_____

_____

_____

_____

_____

_____

_____

_____

_____

_____

_____

_____

_____

_____

_____

_____

NOTES

Speaker _____ *Date* _____

Topic/Title _____ *Place/Event* _____

Reference/Text _____

_____

_____

_____

_____

_____

_____

_____

_____

_____

_____

_____

_____

_____

_____

_____

_____

_____

_____

_____

_____

_____

_____

_____

_____

_____

_____

_____

_____

NOTES

Speaker _____ Date _____

Topic/Title _____ Place/Event _____

Reference/Text _____

_____

_____

_____

_____

_____

_____

_____

_____

_____

_____

_____

_____

_____

_____

_____

_____

_____

_____

_____

_____

_____

_____

_____

_____

_____

_____

_____

_____

_____

_____

NOTES

Speaker _____ *Date* _____

Topic/Title _____ *Place/Event* _____

Reference/Text _____

_____

_____

_____

_____

_____

_____

_____

_____

_____

_____

_____

_____

_____

_____

_____

_____

_____

_____

_____

_____

_____

_____

_____

_____

_____

_____

NOTES

Speaker _____ *Date* _____

Topic/Title _____ *Place/Event* _____

Reference/Text _____

_____

_____

_____

_____

_____

_____

_____

_____

_____

_____

_____

_____

_____

_____

_____

_____

_____

_____

_____

_____

_____

_____

_____

_____

_____

_____

_____

_____

_____

NOTES

Speaker _____ *Date* _____

Topic/Title _____ *Place/Event* _____

Reference/Text _____

_____

_____

_____

_____

_____

_____

_____

_____

_____

_____

_____

_____

_____

_____

_____

_____

_____

_____

_____

_____

_____

_____

_____

_____

_____

_____

_____

NOTES

Speaker _____ *Date* _____

Topic/Title _____ *Place/Event* _____

Reference/Text _____

_____

_____

_____

_____

_____

_____

_____

_____

_____

_____

_____

_____

_____

_____

_____

_____

_____

_____

_____

_____

_____

_____

_____

_____

_____

_____

_____

_____

_____

_____

_____

NOTES

Speaker _____ *Date* _____

Topic/Title _____ *Place/Event* _____

Reference/Text _____

_____

_____

_____

_____

_____

_____

_____

_____

_____

_____

_____

_____

_____

_____

_____

_____

_____

_____

_____

_____

_____

_____

_____

_____

_____

_____

NOTES

Speaker _____ *Date* _____

Topic/Title _____ *Place/Event* _____

Reference/Text _____

_____

_____

_____

_____

_____

_____

_____

_____

_____

_____

_____

_____

_____

_____

_____

_____

_____

_____

_____

_____

_____

_____

_____

_____

_____

NOTES

Speaker _____ *Date* _____

Topic/Title _____ *Place/Event* _____

Reference/Text _____

_____

_____

_____

_____

_____

_____

_____

_____

_____

_____

_____

_____

_____

_____

_____

_____

_____

_____

_____

_____

_____

_____

_____

_____

_____

_____

_____

_____

NOTES

Speaker _____ *Date* _____

Topic/Title _____ *Place/Event* _____

Reference/Text _____

_____

_____

_____

_____

_____

_____

_____

_____

_____

_____

_____

_____

_____

_____

_____

_____

_____

_____

_____

_____

_____

_____

_____

_____

_____

_____

_____

NOTES

Speaker _____ *Date* _____

Topic/Title _____ *Place/Event* _____

Reference/Text _____

_____

_____

_____

_____

_____

_____

_____

_____

_____

_____

_____

_____

_____

_____

_____

_____

_____

_____

_____

_____

_____

_____

_____

_____

_____

_____

_____

_____

NOTES

Speaker _____ *Date* _____

Topic/Title _____ *Place/Event* _____

Reference/Text _____

_____

_____

_____

_____

_____

_____

_____

_____

_____

_____

_____

_____

_____

_____

_____

_____

_____

_____

_____

_____

_____

_____

_____

_____

_____

_____

_____

_____

NOTES

Speaker _____ *Date* _____

Topic/Title _____ *Place/Event* _____

Reference/Text _____

_____

_____

_____

_____

_____

_____

_____

_____

_____

_____

_____

_____

_____

_____

_____

_____

_____

_____

_____

_____

_____

_____

_____

_____

_____

_____

_____

NOTES

Speaker _____ *Date* _____

Topic/Title _____ *Place/Event* _____

Reference/Text _____

NOTES

Speaker _____ *Date* _____

Topic/Title _____ *Place/Event* _____

Reference/Text _____

_____

_____

_____

_____

_____

_____

_____

_____

_____

_____

_____

_____

_____

_____

_____

_____

_____

_____

_____

_____

_____

_____

_____

_____

_____

_____

_____

_____

NOTES

Speaker _____ *Date* _____

Topic/Title _____ *Place/Event* _____

Reference/Text _____

_____

_____

_____

_____

_____

_____

_____

_____

_____

_____

_____

_____

_____

_____

_____

_____

_____

_____

_____

_____

_____

_____

_____

_____

_____

_____

_____

_____

_____

NOTES

Speaker _____ *Date* _____

Topic/Title _____ *Place/Event* _____

Reference/Text _____

_____

_____

_____

_____

_____

_____

_____

_____

_____

_____

_____

_____

_____

_____

_____

_____

_____

_____

_____

_____

_____

_____

_____

_____

_____

_____

NOTES

Speaker _____ *Date* _____

Topic/Title _____ *Place/Event* _____

Reference/Text _____

_____

_____

_____

_____

_____

_____

_____

_____

_____

_____

_____

_____

_____

_____

_____

_____

_____

_____

_____

_____

_____

_____

_____

_____

_____

_____

_____

_____

_____

_____

_____

NOTES

Speaker _____ *Date* _____

Topic/Title _____ *Place/Event* _____

Reference/Text _____

_____

_____

_____

_____

_____

_____

_____

_____

_____

_____

_____

_____

_____

_____

_____

_____

_____

_____

_____

_____

_____

_____

_____

NOTES

Speaker _____ *Date* _____

Topic/Title _____ *Place/Event* _____

Reference/Text _____

_____

_____

_____

_____

_____

_____

_____

_____

_____

_____

_____

_____

_____

_____

_____

_____

_____

_____

_____

_____

_____

_____

_____

_____

_____

_____

_____

_____

_____

NOTES

Speaker _____ *Date* _____

Topic/Title _____ *Place/Event* _____

Reference/Text _____

NOTES

Speaker _____ *Date* _____

Topic/Title _____ *Place/Event* _____

Reference/Text _____

_____

_____

_____

_____

_____

_____

_____

_____

_____

_____

_____

_____

_____

_____

_____

_____

_____

_____

_____

_____

_____

_____

_____

_____

_____

_____

_____

_____

_____

_____

_____

_____

NOTES

Speaker _____ *Date* _____

Topic/Title _____ *Place/Event* _____

Reference/Text _____

NOTES

Speaker _____ *Date* _____

Topic/Title _____ *Place/Event* _____

Reference/Text _____

_____

_____

_____

_____

_____

_____

_____

_____

_____

_____

_____

_____

_____

_____

_____

_____

_____

_____

_____

_____

_____

_____

_____

_____

_____

_____

_____

_____

NOTES

Speaker _____ *Date* _____

Topic/Title _____ *Place/Event* _____

Reference/Text _____

_____

_____

_____

_____

_____

_____

_____

_____

_____

_____

_____

_____

_____

_____

_____

_____

_____

_____

_____

_____

_____

_____

_____

NOTES

Speaker _____ *Date* _____

Topic/Title _____ *Place/Event* _____

Reference/Text _____

_____ _____

_____

_____

_____

_____

_____

_____

_____

_____

_____

_____

_____

_____

_____

_____

_____

_____

_____

_____

_____

_____

_____

_____

_____

_____

_____

_____

_____

NOTES

Speaker _____ *Date* _____

Topic/Title _____ *Place/Event* _____

Reference/Text _____

_____

_____

_____

_____

_____

_____

_____

_____

_____

_____

_____

_____

_____

_____

_____

_____

_____

_____

_____

_____

_____

_____

_____

_____

_____

_____

_____

_____

NOTES

Speaker _____ *Date* _____

Topic/Title _____ *Place/Event* _____

Reference/Text _____

_____ _____

_____

_____

_____

_____

_____

_____

_____

_____

_____

_____

_____

_____

_____

_____

_____

_____

_____

_____

_____

_____

_____

_____

_____

_____

_____

NOTES

Speaker _____ Date _____

Topic/Title _____ Place/Event _____

Reference/Text _____

_____

_____

_____

_____

_____

_____

_____

_____

_____

_____

_____

_____

_____

_____

_____

_____

_____

_____

_____

_____

_____

_____

_____

_____

_____

_____

_____

NOTES

Speaker _____ *Date* _____

Topic/Title _____ *Place/Event* _____

Reference/Text _____

_____

_____

_____

_____

_____

_____

_____

_____

_____

_____

_____

_____

_____

_____

_____

_____

_____

_____

_____

_____

_____

_____

_____

_____

_____

_____

_____

_____

_____

_____

_____

NOTES

Speaker _____ Date _____

Topic/Title _____ Place/Event _____

Reference/Text _____

_____

_____

_____

_____

_____

_____

_____

_____

_____

_____

_____

_____

_____

_____

_____

_____

_____

_____

_____

_____

_____

_____

_____

_____

_____

_____

_____

NOTES

Speaker _____ *Date* _____

Topic/Title _____ *Place/Event* _____

Reference/Text _____

_____
_____
_____
_____
_____
_____
_____
_____
_____
_____
_____
_____
_____
_____
_____
_____
_____
_____
_____
_____
_____
_____
_____
_____
_____
_____
_____
_____
_____
_____
_____
_____

NOTES

Speaker _____ *Date* _____

Topic/Title _____ *Place/Event* _____

Reference/Text _____

_____

_____

_____

_____

_____

_____

_____

_____

_____

_____

_____

_____

_____

_____

_____

_____

_____

_____

_____

_____

_____

_____

_____

_____

_____

_____

NOTES

Speaker _____ *Date* _____

Topic/Title _____ *Place/Event* _____

Reference/Text _____

_____

_____

_____

_____

_____

_____

_____

_____

_____

_____

_____

_____

_____

_____

_____

_____

_____

_____

_____

_____

_____

_____

_____

_____

_____

_____

_____

_____

NOTES

Speaker _____ *Date* _____

Topic/Title _____ *Place/Event* _____

Reference/Text _____

_____

_____

_____

_____

_____

_____

_____

_____

_____

_____

_____

_____

_____

_____

_____

_____

_____

_____

_____

_____

_____

_____

_____

_____

_____

_____

_____

NOTES

Speaker _____ *Date* _____

Topic/Title _____ *Place/Event* _____

Reference/Text _____

NOTES

Speaker _____ *Date* _____

Topic/Title _____ *Place/Event* _____

Reference/Text _____

_____

_____

_____

_____

_____

_____

_____

_____

_____

_____

_____

_____

_____

_____

_____

_____

_____

_____

_____

_____

_____

_____

_____

_____

_____

NOTES

Speaker _____ *Date* _____

Topic/Title _____ *Place/Event* _____

Reference/Text _____

_____
_____
_____
_____
_____
_____
_____
_____
_____
_____
_____
_____
_____
_____
_____
_____
_____
_____
_____
_____
_____
_____
_____
_____
_____
_____
_____
_____
_____

NOTES

Speaker _____ *Date* _____

Topic/Title _____ *Place/Event* _____

Reference/Text _____

_____

_____

_____

_____

_____

_____

_____

_____

_____

_____

_____

_____

_____

_____

_____

_____

_____

_____

_____

_____

_____

_____

_____

_____

_____

_____

_____

_____

NOTES

Speaker _____ *Date* _____

Topic/Title _____ *Place/Event* _____

Reference/Text _____

_____
_____
_____
_____
_____
_____
_____
_____
_____
_____
_____
_____
_____
_____
_____
_____
_____
_____
_____
_____
_____
_____
_____
_____
_____
_____
_____

NOTES

Speaker _____ *Date* _____

Topic/Title _____ *Place/Event* _____

Reference/Text _____

_____

_____

_____

_____

_____

_____

_____

_____

_____

_____

_____

_____

_____

_____

_____

_____

_____

_____

_____

_____

_____

_____

_____

_____

_____

_____

_____

_____

NOTES

Speaker _____ *Date* _____

Topic/Title _____ *Place/Event* _____

Reference/Text _____

_____

_____

_____

_____

_____

_____

_____

_____

_____

_____

_____

_____

_____

_____

_____

_____

_____

_____

_____

_____

_____

_____

_____

_____

_____

_____

_____

_____

_____

_____

_____

_____

NOTES

Speaker _____ *Date* _____

Topic/Title _____ *Place/Event* _____

Reference/Text _____

_____

_____

_____

_____

_____

_____

_____

_____

_____

_____

_____

_____

_____

_____

_____

_____

_____

_____

_____

_____

_____

_____

_____

_____

_____

_____

_____

NOTES

Speaker _____ *Date* _____

Topic/Title _____ *Place/Event* _____

Reference/Text _____

_____

_____

_____

_____

_____

_____

_____

_____

_____

_____

_____

_____

_____

_____

_____

_____

_____

_____

_____

_____

_____

_____

_____

_____

_____

_____

_____

_____

_____

_____

NOTES

Speaker _____ Date _____

Topic/Title _____ Place/Event _____

Reference/Text _____

_____

_____

_____

_____

_____

_____

_____

_____

_____

_____

_____

_____

_____

_____

_____

_____

_____

_____

_____

_____

_____

_____

_____

_____

_____

_____

NOTES

Speaker _____ *Date* _____

Topic/Title _____ *Place/Event* _____

Reference/Text _____

_____

_____

_____

_____

_____

_____

_____

_____

_____

_____

_____

_____

_____

_____

_____

_____

_____

_____

_____

_____

_____

_____

_____

_____

_____

_____

_____

_____

_____

NOTES

Speaker _____ *Date* _____

Topic/Title _____ *Place/Event* _____

Reference/Text _____

NOTES

Speaker _____ *Date* _____

Topic/Title _____ *Place/Event* _____

Reference/Text _____

_____

_____

_____

_____

_____

_____

_____

_____

_____

_____

_____

_____

_____

_____

_____

_____

_____

_____

_____

_____

_____

_____

_____

_____

_____

_____

_____

_____

_____

_____

NOTES

Speaker _____ *Date* _____

Topic/Title _____ *Place/Event* _____

Reference/Text _____

_____

_____

_____

_____

_____

_____

_____

_____

_____

_____

_____

_____

_____

_____

_____

_____

_____

_____

_____

_____

_____

_____

_____

_____

_____

_____

_____

NOTES

Speaker _____ *Date* _____

Topic/Title _____ *Place/Event* _____

Reference/Text _____

_____

_____

_____

_____

_____

_____

_____

_____

_____

_____

_____

_____

_____

_____

_____

_____

_____

_____

_____

_____

_____

_____

_____

_____

_____

_____

_____

_____

_____

_____

NOTES

Speaker _____ *Date* _____

Topic/Title _____ *Place/Event* _____

Reference/Text _____

_____

_____

_____

_____

_____

_____

_____

_____

_____

_____

_____

_____

_____

_____

_____

_____

_____

_____

_____

_____

_____

_____

_____

_____

NOTES

Speaker _____ *Date* _____

Topic/Title _____ *Place/Event* _____

Reference/Text _____

_____

_____

_____

_____

_____

_____

_____

_____

_____

_____

_____

_____

_____

_____

_____

_____

_____

_____

_____

_____

_____

_____

_____

_____

_____

_____

_____

_____

_____

_____

_____

_____

NOTES

Speaker _____ *Date* _____

Topic/Title _____ *Place/Event* _____

Reference/Text _____

_____

_____

_____

_____

_____

_____

_____

_____

_____

_____

_____

_____

_____

_____

_____

_____

_____

_____

_____

_____

_____

_____

_____

_____

_____

_____

NOTES

Speaker _____ *Date* _____

Topic/Title _____ *Place/Event* _____

Reference/Text _____

NOTES

Speaker _____ *Date* _____

Topic/Title _____ *Place/Event* _____

Reference/Text _____

_____

_____

_____

_____

_____

_____

_____

_____

_____

_____

_____

_____

_____

_____

_____

_____

_____

_____

_____

_____

_____

_____

_____

_____

_____

_____

NOTES

Speaker _____ *Date* _____

Topic/Title _____ *Place/Event* _____

Reference/Text _____

_____
_____
_____
_____
_____
_____
_____
_____
_____
_____
_____
_____
_____
_____
_____
_____
_____
_____
_____
_____
_____
_____
_____
_____
_____
_____
_____
_____
_____

NOTES

Speaker _____ Date _____

Topic/Title _____ Place/Event _____

Reference/Text _____

_____

_____

_____

_____

_____

_____

_____

_____

_____

_____

_____

_____

_____

_____

_____

_____

_____

_____

_____

_____

_____

_____

_____

_____

_____

_____

_____

NOTES

Speaker _____ *Date* _____

Topic/Title _____ *Place/Event* _____

Reference/Text _____

_____ _____

_____

_____

_____

_____

_____

_____

_____

_____

_____

_____

_____

_____

_____

_____

_____

_____

_____

_____

_____

_____

_____

_____

_____

_____

_____

_____

_____

NOTES

Speaker _____ *Date* _____

Topic/Title _____ *Place/Event* _____

Reference/Text _____

_____

_____

_____

_____

_____

_____

_____

_____

_____

_____

_____

_____

_____

_____

_____

_____

_____

_____

_____

_____

_____

_____

_____

_____

_____

_____

_____

_____

NOTES

Speaker _____ *Date* _____

Topic/Title _____ *Place/Event* _____

Reference/Text _____

_____ _____

_____

_____

_____

_____

_____

_____

_____

_____

_____

_____

_____

_____

_____

_____

_____

_____

_____

_____

_____

_____

_____

_____

_____

_____

_____

_____

NOTES

Speaker _____ *Date* _____

Topic/Title _____ *Place/Event* _____

Reference/Text _____

_____

_____

_____

_____

_____

_____

_____

_____

_____

_____

_____

_____

_____

_____

_____

_____

_____

_____

_____

_____

_____

_____

_____

_____

_____

_____

_____

_____

_____

_____

NOTES

Speaker _____ *Date* _____

Topic/Title _____ *Place/Event* _____

Reference/Text _____

_____

_____

_____

_____

_____

_____

_____

_____

_____

_____

_____

_____

_____

_____

_____

_____

_____

_____

_____

_____

_____

_____

_____

_____

_____

_____

NOTES

Speaker _____ *Date* _____

Topic/Title _____ *Place/Event* _____

Reference/Text _____

_____

_____

_____

_____

_____

_____

_____

_____

_____

_____

_____

_____

_____

_____

_____

_____

_____

_____

_____

_____

_____

_____

_____

_____

_____

_____

_____

NOTES

Speaker _____ *Date* _____

Topic/Title _____ *Place/Event* _____

Reference/Text _____

NOTES

Speaker _____ *Date* _____

Topic/Title _____ *Place/Event* _____

_____ *Reference/Text* _____

_____

_____

_____

_____

_____

_____

_____

_____

_____

_____

_____

_____

_____

_____

_____

_____

_____

_____

_____

_____

_____

_____

_____

_____

_____

_____

_____

NOTES

Speaker _____ *Date* _____

Topic/Title _____ *Place/Event* _____

Reference/Text _____

_____

_____

_____

_____

_____

_____

_____

_____

_____

_____

_____

_____

_____

_____

_____

_____

_____

_____

_____

_____

_____

_____

_____

_____

_____

_____

_____

_____

_____

NOTES

Speaker _____ *Date* _____

Topic/Title _____ *Place/Event* _____

Reference/Text _____

_____

_____

_____

_____

_____

_____

_____

_____

_____

_____

_____

_____

_____

_____

_____

_____

_____

_____

_____

_____

_____

_____

_____

_____

_____

_____

_____

_____

_____

_____

_____

_____

_____

NOTES

Speaker _____ *Date* _____

Topic/Title _____ *Place/Event* _____

Reference/Text _____

_____

_____

_____

_____

_____

_____

_____

_____

_____

_____

_____

_____

_____

_____

_____

_____

_____

_____

_____

_____

_____

_____

_____

_____

_____

_____

_____

_____

_____

NOTES

Speaker _____ *Date* _____

Topic/Title _____ *Place/Event* _____

Reference/Text _____

_____

_____

_____

_____

_____

_____

_____

_____

_____

_____

_____

_____

_____

_____

_____

_____

_____

_____

_____

_____

_____

_____

_____

_____

_____

_____

_____

_____

NOTES

Speaker _____ *Date* _____

Topic/Title _____ *Place/Event* _____

Reference/Text _____

_____

_____

_____

_____

_____

_____

_____

_____

_____

_____

_____

_____

_____

_____

_____

_____

_____

_____

_____

_____

_____

_____

_____

_____

_____

_____

_____

_____

_____

NOTES

Speaker _____ *Date* _____

Topic/Title _____ *Place/Event* _____

Reference/Text _____

_____

_____

_____

_____

_____

_____

_____

_____

_____

_____

_____

_____

_____

_____

_____

_____

_____

_____

_____

_____

_____

_____

_____

NOTES

Speaker _____ *Date* _____

Topic/Title _____ *Place/Event* _____

Reference/Text _____

_____

_____

_____

_____

_____

_____

_____

_____

_____

_____

_____

_____

_____

_____

_____

_____

_____

_____

_____

_____

_____

_____

_____

_____

_____

_____

_____

_____

NOTES

Speaker _____ *Date* _____

Topic/Title _____ *Place/Event* _____

Reference/Text _____

NOTES

Speaker _____ *Date* _____

Topic/Title _____ *Place/Event* _____

Reference/Text _____

_____

_____

_____

_____

_____

_____

_____

_____

_____

_____

_____

_____

_____

_____

_____

_____

_____

_____

_____

_____

_____

_____

_____

_____

_____

_____

_____

NOTES

Speaker _____ *Date* _____

Topic/Title _____ *Place/Event* _____

Reference/Text _____

_____

_____

_____

_____

_____

_____

_____

_____

_____

_____

_____

_____

_____

_____

_____

_____

_____

_____

_____

_____

_____

_____

_____

_____

_____

_____

NOTES

Speaker _____ *Date* _____

Topic/Title _____ *Place/Event* _____

Reference/Text _____

NOTES

Speaker _____ Date _____

Topic/Title _____ Place/Event _____

Reference/Text _____

_____

_____

_____

_____

_____

_____

_____

_____

_____

_____

_____

_____

_____

_____

_____

_____

_____

_____

_____

_____

_____

_____

_____

_____

_____

_____

_____

_____

NOTES

Speaker _____ *Date* _____

Topic/Title _____ *Place/Event* _____

Reference/Text _____

_____
_____
_____
_____
_____
_____
_____
_____
_____
_____
_____
_____
_____
_____
_____
_____
_____
_____
_____
_____
_____
_____
_____
_____
_____
_____
_____
_____
_____
_____
_____
_____
_____

NOTES

Speaker _____ *Date* _____

Topic/Title _____ *Place/Event* _____

Reference/Text _____

_____

_____

_____

_____

_____

_____

_____

_____

_____

_____

_____

_____

_____

_____

_____

_____

_____

_____

_____

_____

_____

_____

_____

_____

_____

_____

NOTES

Speaker _____ *Date* _____

Topic/Title _____ *Place/Event* _____

Reference/Text _____

_____

_____

_____

_____

_____

_____

_____

_____

_____

_____

_____

_____

_____

_____

_____

_____

_____

_____

_____

_____

_____

_____

_____

_____

_____

_____

_____

_____

_____

_____

_____

NOTES

Speaker _____ *Date* _____

Topic/Title _____ *Place/Event* _____

Reference/Text _____

_____

_____

_____

_____

_____

_____

_____

_____

_____

_____

_____

_____

_____

_____

_____

_____

_____

_____

_____

_____

_____

_____

_____

_____

_____

_____

NOTES

Speaker _____ *Date* _____

Topic/Title _____ *Place/Event* _____

Reference/Text _____

_____

_____

_____

_____

_____

_____

_____

_____

_____

_____

_____

_____

_____

_____

_____

_____

_____

_____

_____

_____

_____

_____

_____

_____

_____

_____

_____

_____

_____

_____

_____

NOTES

Speaker _____ Date _____

Topic/Title _____ Place/Event _____

Reference/Text _____

NOTES

Speaker _____ *Date* _____

Topic/Title _____ *Place/Event* _____

Reference/Text _____

_____

_____

_____

_____

_____

_____

_____

_____

_____

_____

_____

_____

_____

_____

_____

_____

_____

_____

_____

_____

_____

_____

_____

_____

_____

_____

_____

_____

_____

_____

NOTES

Speaker _____ *Date* _____

Topic/Title _____ *Place/Event* _____

Reference/Text _____

_____

_____

_____

_____

_____

_____

_____

_____

_____

_____

_____

_____

_____

_____

_____

_____

_____

_____

_____

_____

_____

_____

_____

_____

_____

_____

NOTES

Speaker _____ *Date* _____

Topic/Title _____ *Place/Event* _____

Reference/Text _____

_____

_____

_____

_____

_____

_____

_____

_____

_____

_____

_____

_____

_____

_____

_____

_____

_____

_____

_____

_____

_____

_____

_____

_____

_____

_____

_____

_____

_____

NOTES

Speaker _____ *Date* _____

Topic/Title _____ *Place/Event* _____

Reference/Text _____

_____

_____

_____

_____

_____

_____

_____

_____

_____

_____

_____

_____

_____

_____

_____

_____

_____

_____

_____

_____

_____

_____

_____

_____

_____

_____

_____

NOTES

Speaker _____ *Date* _____

Topic/Title _____ *Place/Event* _____

Reference/Text _____

_____

_____

_____

_____

_____

_____

_____

_____

_____

_____

_____

_____

_____

_____

_____

_____

_____

_____

_____

_____

_____

_____

_____

_____

_____

_____

_____

_____

NOTES

Speaker _____ *Date* _____

Topic/Title _____ *Place/Event* _____

Reference/Text _____

_____

_____

_____

_____

_____

_____

_____

_____

_____

_____

_____

_____

_____

_____

_____

_____

_____

_____

_____

_____

_____

_____

_____

_____

_____

_____

_____

_____

_____

_____

NOTES

Speaker _____ Date _____

Topic/Title _____ Place/Event _____

Reference/Text _____

_____

_____

_____

_____

_____

_____

_____

_____

_____

_____

_____

_____

_____

_____

_____

_____

_____

_____

_____

_____

_____

_____

_____

_____

_____

_____

_____

_____

NOTES

Speaker _____ *Date* _____

Topic/Title _____ *Place/Event* _____

Reference/Text _____

_____

_____

_____

_____

_____

_____

_____

_____

_____

_____

_____

_____

_____

_____

_____

_____

_____

_____

_____

_____

_____

_____

_____

_____

NOTES

Speaker _____ Date _____

Topic/Title _____ Place/Event _____

Reference/Text _____

_____
_____
_____
_____
_____
_____
_____
_____
_____
_____
_____
_____
_____
_____
_____
_____
_____
_____
_____
_____
_____
_____
_____
_____
_____
_____
_____
_____
_____
_____

NOTES

Speaker _____ *Date* _____

Topic/Title _____ *Place/Event* _____

Reference/Text _____

_____

_____

_____

_____

_____

_____

_____

_____

_____

_____

_____

_____

_____

_____

_____

_____

_____

_____

_____

_____

_____

_____

_____

_____

_____

_____

_____

_____

_____

_____

_____

_____

NOTES

Speaker _____ *Date* _____

Topic/Title _____ *Place/Event* _____

Reference/Text _____

_____

_____

_____

_____

_____

_____

_____

_____

_____

_____

_____

_____

_____

_____

_____

_____

_____

_____

_____

_____

_____

_____

_____

_____

_____

_____

_____

_____

NOTES

Speaker _____ *Date* _____

Topic/Title _____ *Place/Event* _____

Reference/Text _____

_____

_____

_____

_____

_____

_____

_____

_____

_____

_____

_____

_____

_____

_____

_____

_____

_____

_____

_____

_____

_____

_____

_____

_____

_____

NOTES

Speaker _____ *Date* _____

Topic/Title _____ *Place/Event* _____

Reference/Text _____

_____

_____

_____

_____

_____

_____

_____

_____

_____

_____

_____

_____

_____

_____

_____

_____

_____

_____

_____

_____

_____

_____

_____

_____

_____

_____

_____

_____

_____

_____

NOTES

Speaker _____ *Date* _____

Topic/Title _____ *Place/Event* _____

Reference/Text _____

_____

_____

_____

_____

_____

_____

_____

_____

_____

_____

_____

_____

_____

_____

_____

_____

_____

_____

_____

_____

_____

_____

_____

_____

_____

NOTES

Speaker _____ *Date* _____

Topic/Title _____ *Place/Event* _____

Reference/Text _____

_____
_____
_____
_____
_____
_____
_____
_____
_____
_____
_____
_____
_____
_____
_____
_____
_____
_____
_____
_____
_____
_____
_____
_____
_____
_____
_____
_____
_____
_____
_____
_____
_____

NOTES

Speaker _____ *Date* _____

Topic/Title _____ *Place/Event* _____

Reference/Text _____

_____

_____

_____

_____

_____

_____

_____

_____

_____

_____

_____

_____

_____

_____

_____

_____

_____

_____

_____

_____

_____

_____

_____

_____

_____

_____

_____

_____

NOTES

Speaker _____ *Date* _____

Topic/Title _____ *Place/Event* _____

Reference/Text _____

_____

_____

_____

_____

_____

_____

_____

_____

_____

_____

_____

_____

_____

_____

_____

_____

_____

_____

_____

_____

_____

_____

_____

_____

_____

_____

_____

_____

_____

_____

_____

_____

_____

_____

NOTES

Speaker _____ *Date* _____

Topic/Title _____ *Place/Event* _____

Reference/Text _____

_____

_____

_____

_____

_____

_____

_____

_____

_____

_____

_____

_____

_____

_____

_____

_____

_____

_____

_____

_____

_____

_____

_____

_____

_____

_____

_____

NOTES

Speaker _____ *Date* _____

Topic/Title _____ *Place/Event* _____

Reference/Text _____

_____

_____

_____

_____

_____

_____

_____

_____

_____

_____

_____

_____

_____

_____

_____

_____

_____

_____

_____

_____

_____

_____

_____

_____

_____

_____

_____

_____

NOTES

Speaker _____ *Date* _____

Topic/Title _____ *Place/Event* _____

Reference/Text _____

_____

_____

_____

_____

_____

_____

_____

_____

_____

_____

_____

_____

_____

_____

_____

_____

_____

_____

_____

_____

_____

_____

_____

_____

_____

_____

_____

_____

NOTES

Speaker _____ *Date* _____

Topic/Title _____ *Place/Event* _____

Reference/Text _____

_____

_____

_____

_____

_____

_____

_____

_____

_____

_____

_____

_____

_____

_____

_____

_____

_____

_____

_____

_____

_____

_____

_____

_____

_____

_____

_____

_____

NOTES

Speaker _____ *Date* _____

Topic/Title _____ *Place/Event* _____

Reference/Text _____

_____

_____

_____

_____

_____

_____

_____

_____

_____

_____

_____

_____

_____

_____

_____

_____

_____

_____

_____

_____

_____

_____

_____

_____

_____

_____

_____

NOTES

Speaker _____ *Date* _____

Topic/Title _____ *Place/Event* _____

Reference/Text _____

_____

_____

_____

_____

_____

_____

_____

_____

_____

_____

_____

_____

_____

_____

_____

_____

_____

_____

_____

_____

_____

_____

_____

_____

_____

_____

_____

_____

_____

_____

NOTES

Speaker _____ Date _____

Topic/Title _____ Place/Event _____

Reference/Text _____

_____

_____

_____

_____

_____

_____

_____

_____

_____

_____

_____

_____

_____

_____

_____

_____

_____

_____

_____

_____

_____

_____

_____

_____

_____

_____

NOTES

Speaker _____ *Date* _____

Topic/Title _____ *Place/Event* _____

Reference/Text _____

_____

_____

_____

_____

_____

_____

_____

_____

_____

_____

_____

_____

_____

_____

_____

_____

_____

_____

_____

_____

_____

_____

_____

_____

_____

_____

NOTES

Speaker _____ *Date* _____

Topic/Title _____ *Place/Event* _____

Reference/Text _____

_____

_____

_____

_____

_____

_____

_____

_____

_____

_____

_____

_____

_____

_____

_____

_____

_____

_____

_____

_____

_____

_____

_____

_____

NOTES

Speaker _____ *Date* _____

Topic/Title _____ *Place/Event* _____

Reference/Text _____

_____

_____

_____

_____

_____

_____

_____

_____

_____

_____

_____

_____

_____

_____

_____

_____

_____

_____

_____

_____

_____

_____

_____

_____

_____

_____

_____

_____

_____

_____

_____

_____

_____

_____

_____

SCRIPTURE REFERENCE LOG

SCRIPTURE REFERENCE LOG

GENESIS

Reference/Text	Date	Page	Topic/Title

EXODUS

Reference/Text	Date	Page	Topic/Title

LEVITICUS

Reference/Text	Date	Page	Topic/Title

NUMBERS

Reference/Text	Date	Page	Topic/Title

Scripture Reference Log

Deuteronomy

Reference/Text	Date	Page	Topic/Title

Joshua

Reference/Text	Date	Page	Topic/Title

Judges

Reference/Text	Date	Page	Topic/Title

Ruth

Reference/Text	Date	Page	Topic/Title

Scripture Reference Log

I Samuel

Reference/Text	Date	Page	Topic/Title

II Samuel

Reference/Text	Date	Page	Topic/Title

I Kings

Reference/Text	Date	Page	Topic/Title

II Kings

Reference/Text	Date	Page	Topic/Title

SCRIPTURE REFERENCE LOG

I CHRONICLES

Reference/Text	Date	Page	Topic/Title

II CHRONICLES

Reference/Text	Date	Page	Topic/Title

EZRA

Reference/Text	Date	Page	Topic/Title

NEHEMIAH

Reference/Text	Date	Page	Topic/Title

SCRIPTURE REFERENCE LOG

ESTHER

Reference/Text	Date	Page	Topic/Title

JOB

Reference/Text	Date	Page	Topic/Title

PSALMS

Reference/Text	Date	Page	Topic/Title

PROVERBS

Reference/Text	Date	Page	Topic/Title

SCRIPTURE REFERENCE LOG

ECCLESIASTES

Reference/Text	Date	Page	Topic/Title

SONG OF SOLOMON

Reference/Text	Date	Page	Topic/Title

ISAIAH

Reference/Text	Date	Page	Topic/Title

JEREMIAH

Reference/Text	Date	Page	Topic/Title

Scripture Reference Log

Lamentations

Reference/Text	Date	Page	Topic/Title

Ezekiel

Reference/Text	Date	Page	Topic/Title

Daniel

Reference/Text	Date	Page	Topic/Title

Hosea

Reference/Text	Date	Page	Topic/Title

Scripture Reference Log

Joel

Reference/Text	Date	Page	Topic/Title

Amos

Obadiah

Jonah

Scripture Reference Log

Micah

Reference/Text	Date	Page	Topic/Title

Nahum

Reference/Text	Date	Page	Topic/Title

Habakkuk

Reference/Text	Date	Page	Topic/Title

Zephaniah

Reference/Text	Date	Page	Topic/Title

SCRIPTURE REFERENCE LOG

HAGGAI

Reference/Text	Date	Page	Topic/Title

ZECHARIAH

Reference/Text	Date	Page	Topic/Title

MALACHI

Reference/Text	Date	Page	Topic/Title

SCRIPTURE REFERENCE LOG

MATTHEW

Reference/Text	Date	Page	Topic/Title

MARK

Reference/Text	Date	Page	Topic/Title

LUKE

Reference/Text	Date	Page	Topic/Title

JOHN

Reference/Text	Date	Page	Topic/Title

SCRIPTURE REFERENCE LOG

ACTS

Reference/Text	Date	Page	Topic/Title

ROMANS

I CORINTHIANS

II CORINTHIANS

Scripture Reference Log

GALATIANS

Reference/Text	Date	Page	Topic/Title

EPHESIANS

Reference/Text	Date	Page	Topic/Title

PHILIPPIANS

Reference/Text	Date	Page	Topic/Title

COLOSSIANS

Reference/Text	Date	Page	Topic/Title

Scripture Reference Log

I Thessalonians

Reference/Text	Date	Page	Topic/Title

II Thessalonians

I Timothy

II Timothy

Scripture Reference Log

Titus

Reference/Text	Date	Page	Topic/Title

Philemon

Reference/Text	Date	Page	Topic/Title

Hebrews

Reference/Text	Date	Page	Topic/Title

James

Reference/Text	Date	Page	Topic/Title

SCRIPTURE REFERENCE LOG

I PETER

Reference/Text	Date	Page	Topic/Title

II PETER

Reference/Text	Date	Page	Topic/Title

I JOHN

Reference/Text	Date	Page	Topic/Title

II JOHN

Reference/Text	Date	Page	Topic/Title

SCRIPTURE REFERENCE LOG

III JOHN

Reference/Text	Date	Page	Topic/Title

JUDE

Reference/Text	Date	Page	Topic/Title

REVELATION

Reference/Text	Date	Page	Topic/Title

Humor & Illustrations

HUMOR & ILLUSTRATIONS

HUMOR & ILLUSTRATIONS

HUMOR & ILLUSTRATIONS

HUMOR & ILLUSTRATIONS

MUSIC

Title   *Performer/Composer*

_____   _____

_____   _____

_____   _____

_____   _____

_____   _____

_____   _____

_____   _____

_____   _____

_____   _____

_____   _____

_____   _____

_____   _____

_____   _____

_____   _____

_____   _____

_____   _____

_____   _____

_____   _____

_____   _____

_____   _____

_____   _____

_____   _____

MUSIC

Title   Performer/Composer

_____   _____
_____   _____
_____   _____
_____   _____
_____   _____
_____   _____
_____   _____
_____   _____
_____   _____
_____   _____
_____   _____
_____   _____
_____   _____
_____   _____
_____   _____
_____   _____
_____   _____
_____   _____
_____   _____
_____   _____
_____   _____
_____   _____

MUSIC

Title   *Performer/Composer*

_____   _____

_____   _____

_____   _____

_____   _____

_____   _____

_____   _____

_____   _____

_____   _____

_____   _____

_____   _____

_____   _____

_____   _____

_____   _____

_____   _____

_____   _____

_____   _____

_____   _____

_____   _____

_____   _____

_____   _____

_____   _____

_____   _____

_____   _____

MUSIC

Title   *Performer/Composer*

_____   _____

_____   _____

_____   _____

_____   _____

_____   _____

_____   _____

_____   _____

_____   _____

_____   _____

_____   _____

_____   _____

_____   _____

_____   _____

_____   _____

_____   _____

_____   _____

_____   _____

_____   _____

_____   _____

_____   _____

Music

Title   *Performer/Composer*

_____   _____
_____   _____
_____   _____
_____   _____
_____   _____
_____   _____
_____   _____
_____   _____
_____   _____
_____   _____
_____   _____
_____   _____
_____   _____
_____   _____
_____   _____
_____   _____
_____   _____
_____   _____
_____   _____
_____   _____
_____   _____
_____   _____

BOOKS & TAPES

BOOKS & TAPES

BOOKS & TAPES

PRAYER LIST

PRAYER LIST

_____

_____

_____

_____

_____

_____

_____

_____

_____

_____

_____

_____

_____

_____

_____

_____

_____

_____

_____

_____

_____

_____

_____

_____

_____

_____

_____

_____

PRAYER LIST

_____

_____

_____

_____

_____

_____

_____

_____

_____

_____

_____

_____

_____

_____

_____

_____

_____

_____

_____

_____

_____

_____

_____

_____

_____

_____

Scripture Memory Schedule

☐ **WEEK 1**

Enter into His gates with thanksgiving, and into His courts with praise: be thankful unto Him, and bless His name.

For the Lord is good; His mercy is everlasting, and His truth endureth to all generations. Psalm 100:4-5

☐ **WEEK 2**

Behold, the Lord's hand is not shortened, that it cannot save; neither His ear heavy, that it cannot hear: Isaiah 59:1

☐ **WEEK 3**

For verily I say unto you, That whosoever shall say unto this mountain, Be thou removed, and be thou cast into the sea; and shall not doubt in his heart, but shall believe that those things which he saith shall come to pass: he shall have whatsoever he saith.

Therefore I say unto you, What things soever ye desire, when ye pray, believe that ye shall receive them, and ye shall have them. Mark 11:23-24

☐ **WEEK 4**

For therein is the righteousness of God revealed from faith to faith: as it is written, The just shall live by faith. Romans 1:17

☐ **WEEK 5**

Trust in Him at all times; ye people, pour out your heart before Him: God is a refuge for us. Psalm 62:8

☐ **WEEK 6**

And in that day ye shall ask Me nothing. Verily, verily, I say unto you, Whatsoever ye shall ask the Father in My name, He will give it you. John 16:23

☐ **WEEK 7**

Trust in the Lord with all thine heart; and lean not unto thine own understanding.

In all thy ways acknowledge Him, and He shall direct thy paths. Proverbs 3:5-6

☐ **WEEK 8**

The young lions do lack, and suffer hunger: but they that seek the Lord shall not want any good thing. Psalm 34:10

☐ **WEEK 9**

But seek ye first the kingdom of God, and His righteousness; and all these things shall be added unto you. Matthew 6:33

☐ **WEEK 10**

Blessed is the man that walketh not in the counsel of the ungodly, nor standeth in the way of sinners, nor sitteth in the seat of the scornful.

But his delight is in the law of the Lord; and in His law doth he meditate day and night.

And he shall be like a tree planted by the rivers of water, that bringeth forth his fruit in his season; his leaf also shall not wither; and whatsoever he doeth shall prosper. Psalm 1:1-3

SCRIPTURE MEMORY SCHEDULE

☐ WEEK 11

Honour the Lord with thy substance, and with the first fruits of all thine increase:

So shall thy barns be filled with plenty, and thy presses shall burst out with new wine. Proverbs 3:9-10

☐ WEEK 12

Saying, Surely blessing I shall bless thee, and multiplying I will multiply thee. Hebrews 6:14

☐ WEEK 13

And if thou draw out thy soul to the hungry, and satisfy the afflicted soul; then shall thy light rise in obscurity, and thy darkness be as the noon day:

And the Lord shall guide thee continually, and satisfy thy soul in drought, and make fat thy bones: and thou shalt be like a watered garden, and like a spring of water, whose waters fail not. Isaiah 58:10-11

☐ WEEK 14

Beloved, I wish above all things that thou mayest prosper and be in health, even as thy soul prospereth. III John 2

☐ WEEK 15

And ye shall serve the Lord your God, and He shall bless thy bread, and thy water; and I will take sickness away from the midst of thee. Exodus 23:25

☐ WEEK 16

And said, If thou wilt diligently harken to the voice of the Lord thy God, and wilt do that which is right in His sight, and wilt give ear to His commandments, and keep all His statutes, I will put none of these diseases upon thee, which I have brought upon the Egyptians: for I am the Lord that healeth thee. Exodus 15:26

☐ WEEK 17

Who His own self bare our sins in His own body on the tree, that we, being dead to sins, should live unto righteousness: by Whose stripes ye were healed. 1 Peter 2:24

☐ WEEK 18

That it might be fulfilled which was spoken by Esaias the prophet, saying, Himself took our infirmities, and bare our sicknesses. Matthew 8:17

☐ WEEK 19

Jesus Christ the same yesterday, and to day, and for ever. Hebrews 13:8

☐ WEEK 20

Beloved, if our heart condemn us not, then we have confidence toward God.

And whatsoever we ask, we receive of Him, because we keep His commandments, and do those things that are pleasing in His sight. I John 3:21-22

Scripture Memory Schedule

☐ WEEK 21

    In my distress I cried unto the Lord, and He heard me.
Psalm 120:1

☐ WEEK 22

    *In his neck remaineth strength, and sorrow is turned into joy
before him.* Job 41:22

☐ WEEK 23

    *Thou wilt shew me the path of life: in Thy presence is fulness of
joy; at Thy right hand there are pleasures for evermore.* Psalm 16:11

☐ WEEK 24

    *These things have I spoken unto you, that My joy might remain
in you, and that your joy might be full.* John 15:11

☐ WEEK 25

    *For I am persuaded, that neither death, nor life, nor angels, nor
principalities, nor powers, nor things present, nor things to come,*
    *Nor height, nor depth, nor any other creature, shall be able to
separate us from the love of God, which is in Christ Jesus our Lord.*
Romans 8:38-39

☐ WEEK 26

    *For God hath not given us the spirit of fear; but of power, and of
love, and of a sound mind.* II Timothy 1:7

☐ WEEK 27

    *Love worketh no ill to his neighbour: therefore love is the
fulfilling of the law.* Romans 13:10

☐ WEEK 28

    *A new commandment I give unto you, That ye love one another;
as I have loved you, that ye also love one another.*
    *By this shall all men know that ye are My disciples, if ye have
love one to another.* John 13:34-35

☐ WEEK 29

    *I love them that love Me; and those that seek Me early shall find
Me.* Proverbs 8:17

☐ WEEK 30

    *Therefore with joy shall ye draw water out of the wells of
salvation.* Isaiah 12:3

☐ WEEK 31

    *And the ransomed of the Lord shall return, and come to Zion
with songs and everlasting joy upon their heads: they shall obtain joy
and gladness, and sorrow and sighing shall flee away.* Isaiah 35:10

☐ WEEK 32

    Rejoice in the Lord alway: and again I say, Rejoice.
Philippians 4:4

☐ WEEK 33

    *Thy words were found, and I did eat them; and Thy Word was
unto me the joy and rejoicing of mine heart: for I am called by Thy
name, O Lord God of hosts.* Jeremiah 15:16

SCRIPTURE MEMORY SCHEDULE

☐ WEEK 34

Although the fig tree shall not blossom, neither shall fruit be in the vines; the labour of the olive shall fail, and the fields shall yield no meat; the flock shall be cut off from the fold, and there shall be no herd in the stalls:

Yet I will rejoice in the Lord, I will joy in the God of my salvation.

The Lord God is my strength, and He will make my feet like hinds' feet, and he will make me to walk upon mine high places ... Habakkuk 3:17-19

☐ WEEK 35

Now unto Him that is able to keep you from falling, and to present you faultless before the presence of His glory with exceeding joy. Jude 24

☐ WEEK 36

My brethren, count it all joy when ye fall into divers temptations; Knowing this, that the trying of your faith worketh patience. James 1:2-3

☐ WEEK 37

Therefore being justified by faith, we have peace with God through our Lord Jesus Christ. Romans 5:1

☐ WEEK 38

Cast not away, therefore, your confidence, which hath great recompence of reward.

For ye have need of patience, that, after ye have done the will of God, ye might receive the promise. Hebrews 10:35-36

☐ WEEK 39

Rest in the Lord, and wait patiently for Him ... Psalm 37:7

☐ WEEK 40

Fight the good fight of faith, lay hold on eternal life, where unto thou art also called and hath professed a good profession before many witnesses. I Timothy 6:12

☐ WEEK 41

Strengthened with all might, according to His glorious power, unto all patience and longsuffering with joyfulness;

Giving thanks unto the Father, which hath made us meet to be partakers of the inheritance of the saints in light. Colossians 1:11-12

☐ WEEK 42

Call unto me, and I will answer thee, and shew thee great and mighty things, which thou knowest not. Jeremiah 33:3

☐ WEEK 43

The LORD is nigh unto them that are of a broken heart, and saveth such as be of a contrite spirit. Psalm 34:18

☐ WEEK 44

I will not leave you comfortless: I will come to you. John 14:18

☐ WEEK 45

... and, lo, I am with you alway, even unto the end of the world. Matthew 28:20

SCRIPTURE MEMORY SCHEDULE

☐ WEEK 46

... for He hath said, I will never leave thee, nor forsake thee.

So that we may boldly say, The Lord is my helper, and I will not fear what man shall do unto me. Hebrews 13:5-6

☐ WEEK 47

Commit thy way unto the LORD; trust also in Him; and He shall bring it to pass.

And He shall bring forth thy righteousness as the light, and thy judgment as the noonday. Psalm 37:5-6

☐ WEEK 48

But Thou, O LORD, art a shield for me; my glory, and the lifter up of mine head. Psalm 3:3

☐ WEEK 49

Behold, his soul which is lifted up is not upright in him: but the just shall live by his faith. Habakkuk 2:4

☐ WEEK 50

If any of you lack wisdom, let him ask of God, that giveth to all men liberally, and upbraideth not; and it shall be given him.

But let him ask in faith, nothing wavering. For he that wavereth is like a wave of the sea driven with the wind and tossed.

For let not that man think that he shall receive any thing of the Lord.

A double minded man is unstable in all his ways. James 1:5-8

☐ WEEK 51

Jesus said unto him, If thou canst believe, all things are possible to him that believeth. Mark 9:23

☐ WEEK 52

He staggered not at the promise of God through unbelief; but was strong in faith, giving glory to God;

And being fully persuaded that, what He had promised, He was able also to perform. Romans 4:20-21

ONE-YEAR BIBLE READING SCHEDULE

✔	Day	Scripture	✔	Day	Scripture	✔	Day	Scripture
☐	1	Gen.1-3	☐	47	Lev. 10-12	☐	92	Acts 4-6
☐	2	Gen. 4-6	☐	48	Lev. 13-15	☐	93	Acts 7-9
☐	3	Gen.7-9	☐	49	Lev. 16-18	☐	94	Acts 10-12
☐	4	Gen. 10-12	☐	50	Lev. 19-21	☐	95	Acts 13-15
☐	5	Gen. 13-15	☐	51	Lev. 22-24	☐	96	Acts 16-18
☐	6	Gen. 16-18	☐	52	Lev. 25-27	☐	97	Acts 19-21
☐	7	Gen. 19-21				☐	98	Acts 22-24
☐	8	Gen. 22-24	☐	53	Luke 1-3	☐	99	Acts 25-28
☐	9	Gen. 25-27	☐	54	Luke 4-6			
☐	10	Gen. 28-30	☐	55	Luke 7-9	☐	100	Josh. 1-3
☐	11	Gen. 31-33	☐	56	Luke 10-12	☐	101	Josh. 4-6
☐	12	Gen. 34-36	☐	57	Luke 13-15	☐	102	Josh. 7-9
☐	13	Gen. 37-39	☐	58	Luke 16-18	☐	103	Josh. 10-12
☐	14	Gen. 40-42	☐	59	Luke 19-21	☐	104	Josh. 13-15
☐	15	Gen. 43-45	☐	60	Luke 22-24	☐	105	Josh. 16-18
☐	16	Gen. 46-50				☐	106	Josh. 19-21
			☐	61	Num. 1-3	☐	107	Josh. 22-24
☐	17	Matt. 1-3	☐	62	Num. 4-6			
☐	18	Matt. 4-6	☐	63	Num. 7-9	☐	108	Rom. 1-3
☐	19	Matt. 7-9	☐	64	Num. 10-12	☐	109	Rom. 4-6
☐	20	Matt. 10-12	☐	65	Num. 13-15	☐	110	Rom. 7-9
☐	21	Matt. 13-15	☐	66	Num. 16-18	☐	111	Rom. 10-12
☐	22	Matt. 16-18	☐	67	Num. 19-21	☐	112	Rom. 13-16
☐	23	Matt. 19-21	☐	68	Num. 22-24			
☐	24	Matt. 22-24	☐	69	Num. 25-27	☐	113	Judg. 1-3
☐	25	Matt. 25-28	☐	70	Num. 28-30	☐	114	Judg. 4-6
			☐	71	Num. 31-33	☐	115	Judg. 7-9
☐	26	Ex. 1-3	☐	72	Num. 34-36	☐	116	Judg. 10-12
☐	27	Ex. 4-6				☐	117	Judg. 13-15
☐	28	Ex. 7-9	☐	73	John 1-3	☐	118	Judg. 16-18
☐	29	Ex. 10-12	☐	74	John 4-6	☐	119	Judg. 19-21
☐	30	Ex. 13-15	☐	75	John 7-9			
☐	31	Ex. 16-18	☐	76	John 10-12	☐	120	Ruth 1-2
☐	32	Ex. 19-21	☐	77	John 13-15	☐	121	Ruth 3-4
☐	33	Ex. 22-24	☐	78	John 16-18			
☐	34	Ex. 25-27	☐	79	John 19-21	☐	122	I Cor. 1-3
☐	35	Ex. 28-30				☐	123	I Cor. 4-6
☐	36	Ex. 31-33	☐	80	Deut. 1-3	☐	124	I Cor. 7-9
☐	37	Ex. 34-36	☐	81	Deut. 4-6	☐	125	I Cor. 10-12
☐	38	Ex. 37-40	☐	82	Deut. 7-9	☐	126	I Cor. 13-16
			☐	83	Deut. 10-12			
☐	39	Mark 1-3	☐	84	Deut. 13-15	☐	127	I Sam. 1-3
☐	40	Mark 4-6	☐	85	Deut. 16-18	☐	128	I Sam. 4-6
☐	41	Mark 7-9	☐	86	Deut. 19-21	☐	129	I Sam. 7-9
☐	42	Mark 10-12	☐	87	Deut. 22-24	☐	130	I Sam. 10-12
☐	43	Mark 13-16	☐	88	Deut. 25-27	☐	131	I Sam. 13-15
			☐	89	Deut. 28-30	☐	132	I Sam. 16-18
☐	44	Lev. 1-3	☐	90	Deut. 31-34	☐	133	I Sam. 19-21
☐	45	Lev. 4-6				☐	134	I Sam. 22-24
☐	46	Lev. 7-9	☐	91	Acts 1-3	☐	135	I Sam. 25-27

ONE-YEAR BIBLE READING SCHEDULE

✔	Day	Scripture	✔	Day	Scripture	✔	Day	Scripture
☐	136	I Sam. 28-31	☐	178	I Chr. 28-29	☐	217	Ps. 1-5
						☐	218	Ps. 6-10
☐	137	II Cor. 1-3	☐	179	Col. 1-4	☐	219	Ps. 11-15
☐	138	II Cor. 4-6				☐	220	Ps. 16-20
☐	139	II Cor. 7-9	☐	180	II Chr. 1-3	☐	221	Ps. 21-25
☐	140	II Cor. 10-13	☐	181	II Chr. 4-6	☐	222	Ps. 26-30
			☐	182	II Chr. 7-9	☐	223	Ps. 31-34
☐	141	II Sam. 1-3	☐	183	II Chr. 10-12	☐	224	Ps. 35-37
☐	142	II Sam. 4-6	☐	184	II Chr. 13-15	☐	225	Ps. 38-41
☐	143	II Sam. 7-9	☐	185	II Chr. 16-18	☐	226	Ps. 42-45
☐	144	II Sam. 10-12	☐	186	II Chr. 19-21	☐	227	Ps. 46-49
☐	145	II Sam. 13-15	☐	187	II Chr. 22-24	☐	228	Ps. 50-53
☐	146	II Sam. 16-18	☐	188	II Chr. 25-27	☐	229	Ps. 54-57
☐	147	II Sam. 19-21	☐	189	II Chr. 28-30	☐	230	Ps. 58-61
☐	148	II Sam. 22-24	☐	190	II Chr. 31-33	☐	231	Ps. 62-65
			☐	191	II Chr. 34-36	☐	232	Ps. 66-68
☐	149	Gal. 1-3				☐	233	Ps. 69-72
☐	150	Gal. 4-6	☐	192	I Thess. 1-5	☐	234	Ps. 73-76
						☐	235	Ps. 77-78
☐	151	I Kin. 1-3	☐	193	II Thess. 1-3	☐	236	Ps. 79-82
☐	152	I Kin. 4-6				☐	237	Ps. 83-86
☐	153	I Kin. 7-9	☐	194	Ezra 1-3	☐	238	Ps. 87-89
☐	154	I Kin. 10-12	☐	195	Ezra 4-6	☐	239	Ps. 90-93
☐	155	I Kin. 13-15	☐	196	Ezra 7-10	☐	240	Ps. 94-97
☐	156	I Kin. 16-18				☐	241	Ps. 98-102
☐	157	I Kin. 19-22	☐	197	Neh. 1-3	☐	242	Ps. 103-104
			☐	198	Neh. 4-6	☐	243	Ps. 105-106
☐	158	Eph. 1-3	☐	199	Neh.7-9	☐	244	Ps. 107-109
☐	159	Eph. 4-6	☐	200	Neh. 10-13	☐	245	Ps. 110-115
						☐	246	Ps. 116-118
☐	160	II Kin. 1-3	☐	201	Esther 1-3	☐	247	Ps. 119-188
☐	161	II Kin. 4-6	☐	202	Esther 4-6	☐	248	Ps. 119:89-176
☐	162	II Kin. 7-9	☐	203	Esther 7-10	☐	249	Ps. 120-127
☐	163	II Kin. 10-12				☐	250	Ps. 128-134
☐	164	II Kin. 13-15	☐	204	Job 1-4	☐	251	Ps. 135-138
☐	165	II Kin. 16-18	☐	205	Job 5-8	☐	252	Ps. 139-142
☐	166	II Kin. 19-21	☐	206	Job 9-12	☐	253	Ps. 143-146
☐	167	II Kin. 22-25	☐	207	Job 13-16	☐	254	Ps. 147-150
			☐	208	Job 17-21			
☐	168	Phil. 1-4	☐	209	Job 22-26	☐	255	Titus, Philem .
			☐	210	Job 27-30			
☐	169	I Chr. 1-3	☐	211	Job 31-34	☐	256	Prov. 1-4
☐	170	I Chr. 4-6	☐	212	Job 35-38	☐	257	Prov. 5-8
☐	171	I Chr. 7-9	☐	213	Job 39-42	☐	258	Prov. 9-12
☐	172	I Chr. 10-12				☐	259	Prov. 13-15
☐	173	I Chr. 13-15	☐	216	II Tim. 1-4	☐	260	Prov. 16-18
☐	174	I Chr. 16-18				☐	261	Prov. 19-21
☐	175	I Chr. 19-21				☐	262	Prov. 22-24
☐	176	I Chr. 22-24				☐	263	Prov. 25-27
☐	177	I Chr. 25-27				☐	264	Prov. 28-31

One-Year Bible Reading Schedule

✔ Day	Scripture	✔ Day	Scripture	✔ Day	Scripture
☐ 265	Heb. 1-4	☐ 309	Jer. 34-36	☐ 349	Jon. 1-4
☐ 266	Heb. 5-7	☐ 310	Jer. 37-39		
☐ 267	Heb. 8-10	☐ 311	Jer. 40-42	☐ 350	Mic. 1-3
☐ 268	Heb. 11-13	☐ 312	Jer. 43-45	☐ 351	Mic. 4-7
		☐ 313	Jer. 46-48		
☐ 269	Eccles. 1- 4	☐ 314	Jer. 49-52	☐ 352	Nah. 1-3
☐ 270	Eccles. 5-8				
☐ 271	Eccles. 9-12	☐ 315	II Pet. 1-3	☐ 353	Hab. 1-3
☐ 272	S. of S. 1-2	☐ 316	Lam. 1-3	☐ 354	Zeph., Hag.
☐ 273	S. of S. 3-4	☐ 317	Lam. 4-5		
☐ 274	S. of S. 5-8			☐ 355	Zech. 1-3
		☐ 318	Ezek. 1-4	☐ 356	Zech. 4-6
☐ 275	James 1-5	☐ 319	Ezek. 5-8	☐ 357	Zech. 7-9
		☐ 320	Ezek. 9-12	☐ 358	Zech.10-14
☐ 276	Is. 1-3	☐ 321	Ezek. 13-15		
☐ 277	Is. 4-7	☐ 322	Ezek. 16-18	☐ 359	Mal. 1-4
☐ 278	Is. 8-10	☐ 323	Ezek. 19-21		
☐ 279	Is. 11-13	☐ 324	Ezek. 22-24	☐ 360	Rev. 1-3
☐ 280	Is. 14-17	☐ 325	Ezek. 25-27	☐ 361	Rev. 4-6
☐ 281	Is. 18-21	☐ 326	Ezek. 28-30	☐ 362	Rev. 7-10
☐ 282	Is. 22-25	☐ 327	Ezek. 31-33	☐ 363	Rev. 11-15
☐ 283	Is. 26-28	☐ 328	Ezek. 34-36	☐ 364	Rev. 16-18
☐ 284	Is. 29-30	☐ 329	Ezek. 37-39	☐ 365	Rev. 19-22
☐ 285	Is. 31-33	☐ 330	Ezek. 40-42		
☐ 286	Is. 34-36	☐ 331	Ezek. 43-45		
☐ 287	Is. 37-39	☐ 332	Ezek. 46-48		
☐ 288	Is. 40-42				
☐ 289	Is. 43-45	☐ 333	I John 1-5		
☐ 290	Is. 46-48				
☐ 291	Is. 49-51	☐ 334	Dan. 1-3		
☐ 292	Is. 52-54	☐ 335	Dan. 4-6		
☐ 293	Is. 55-57	☐ 336	Dan. 7-9		
☐ 294	Is. 58-60	☐ 337	Dan. 10-12		
☐ 295	Is. 61-63				
☐ 296	Is. 64-66	☐ 338	Hos. 1-3		
		☐ 339	Hos. 4-6		
☐ 297	I Pet. 1-5	☐ 340	Hos. 7-9		
		☐ 341	Hos. 10-12		
☐ 298	Jer. 1-3	☐ 342	Hos. 13-14		
☐ 299	Jer. 4-6				
☐ 300	Jer. 7-9	☐ 343	Joel 1-3		
☐ 301	Jer. 10-12				
☐ 302	Jer. 13-15	☐ 344	Amos 1-3		
☐ 303	Jer. 16-18	☐ 345	Amos 4-6		
☐ 304	Jer. 19-21	☐ 346	Amos 7-9		
☐ 305	Jer. 22-24				
☐ 306	Jer. 25-27	☐ 347	Obad.		
☐ 307	Jer. 28-30				
☐ 308	Jer. 31-33	☐ 348	II & III John, Jude		

CONFERENCES, MEETINGS & SPECIAL EVENTS

Date	Description	Place

NAMES & ADDRESSES

Name

Address

Phone   (W)
        (H)

Name

Address

Phone   (W)
        (H)

Name

Address

Phone   (W)
        (H)

Name

Address

Phone   (W)
        (H)

Name

Address

Phone   (W)
        (H)

Name

Address

Phone   (W)
        (H)

Name

Address

Phone   (W)
        (H)

Name

Address

Phone   (W)
        (H)

Name

Address

Phone   (W)
        (H)

Name

Address

Phone   (W)
        (H)

Name

Address

Phone   (W)
        (H)

Name

Address

Phone   (W)
        (H)

Name

Address

Phone   (W)
        (H)

Name

Address

Phone   (W)
        (H)

Name

Address

Phone   (W)
        (H)

Name

Address

Phone   (W)
        (H)

Name

Address

Phone   (W)
        (H)

Name

Address

Phone   (W)
        (H)

A - B - C

Names & Addresses

Name	Name
Address	Address
Phone (W) (H)	Phone (W) (H)
Name	Name
Address	Address
Phone (W) (H)	Phone (W) (H)
Name	Name
Address	Address
Phone (W) (H)	Phone (W) (H)
Name	Name
Address	Address
Phone (W) (H)	Phone (W) (H)
Name	Name
Address	Address
Phone (W) (H)	Phone (W) (H)
Name	Name
Address	Address
Phone (W) (H)	Phone (W) (H)
Name	Name
Address	Address
Phone (W) (H)	Phone (W) (H)
Name	Name
Address	Address
Phone (W) (H)	Phone (W) (H)
Name	Name
Address	Address
Phone (W) (H)	Phone (W) (H)

D - E - F

Names & Addresses

Name	Name
Address	Address
Phone (W) (H)	Phone (W) (H)
Name	Name
Address	Address
Phone (W) (H)	Phone (W) (H)
Name	Name
Address	Address
Phone (W) (H)	Phone (W) (H)
Name	Name
Address	Address
Phone (W) (H)	Phone (W) (H)
Name	Name
Address	Address
Phone (W) (H)	Phone (W) (H)
Name	Name
Address	Address
Phone (W) (H)	Phone (W) (H)
Name	Name
Address	Address
Phone (W) (H)	Phone (W) (H)
Name	Name
Address	Address
Phone (W) (H)	Phone (W) (H)
Name	Name
Address	Address
Phone (W) (H)	Phone (W) (H)

G - H - I

Names & Addresses

Name _____

Address _____

Phone ___ (W) ___ (H)

Name _____

Address _____

Phone ___ (W) ___ (H)

Name _____

Address _____

Phone ___ (W) ___ (H)

Name _____

Address _____

Phone ___ (W) ___ (H)

Name _____

Address _____

Phone ___ (W) ___ (H)

Name _____

Address _____

Phone ___ (W) ___ (H)

Name _____

Address _____

Phone ___ (W) ___ (H)

Name _____

Address _____

Phone ___ (W) ___ (H)

Name _____

Address _____

Phone ___ (W) ___ (H)

Name _____

Address _____

Phone ___ (W) ___ (H)

Name _____

Address _____

Phone ___ (W) ___ (H)

Name _____

Address _____

Phone ___ (W) ___ (H)

Name _____

Address _____

Phone ___ (W) ___ (H)

Name _____

Address _____

Phone ___ (W) ___ (H)

Name _____

Address _____

Phone ___ (W) ___ (H)

Name _____

Address _____

Phone ___ (W) ___ (H)

Name _____

Address _____

Phone ___ (W) ___ (H)

Name _____

Address _____

Phone ___ (W) ___ (H)

J - K - L

NAMES & ADDRESSES

Name	Name
Address	Address
Phone (W) (H)	Phone (W) (H)
Name	Name
Address	Address
Phone (W) (H)	Phone (W) (H)
Name	Name
Address	Address
Phone (W) (H)	Phone (W) (H)
Name	Name
Address	Address
Phone (W) (H)	Phone (W) (H)
Name	Name
Address	Address
Phone (W) (H)	Phone (W) (H)
Name	Name
Address	Address
Phone (W) (H)	Phone (W) (H)
Name	Name
Address	Address
Phone (W) (H)	Phone (W) (H)
Name	Name
Address	Address
Phone (W) (H)	Phone (W) (H)

M - N - O

Names & Addresses

Name	Name
Address	Address
Phone (W) (H)	Phone (W) (H)
Name	Name
Address	Address
Phone (W) (H)	Phone (W) (H)
Name	Name
Address	Address
Phone (W) (H)	Phone (W) (H)
Name	Name
Address	Address
Phone (W) (H)	Phone (W) (H)
Name	Name
Address	Address
Phone (W) (H)	Phone (W) (H)
Name	Name
Address	Address
Phone (W) (H)	Phone (W) (H)
Name	Name
Address	Address
Phone (W) (H)	Phone (W) (H)
Name	Name
Address	Address
Phone (W) (H)	Phone (W) (H)

P - Q - R

Names & Addresses

Name	Name
Address	Address
Phone (W) (H)	Phone (W) (H)
Name	Name
Address	Address
Phone (W) (H)	Phone (W) (H)
Name	Name
Address	Address
Phone (W) (H)	Phone (W) (H)
Name	Name
Address	Address
Phone (W) (H)	Phone (W) (H)
Name	Name
Address	Address
Phone (W) (H)	Phone (W) (H)
Name	Name
Address	Address
Phone (W) (H)	Phone (W) (H)
Name	Name
Address	Address
Phone (W) (H)	Phone (W) (H)
Name	Name
Address	Address
Phone (W) (H)	Phone (W) (H)

S - T - U

Names & Addresses

Name	Name
Address	Address
Phone (W) (H)	Phone (W) (H)
Name	Name
Address	Address
Phone (W) (H)	Phone (W) (H)
Name	Name
Address	Address
Phone (W) (H)	Phone (W) (H)
Name	Name
Address	Address
Phone (W) (H)	Phone (W) (H)
Name	Name
Address	Address
Phone (W) (H)	Phone (W) (H)
Name	Name
Address	Address
Phone (W) (H)	Phone (W) (H)
Name	Name
Address	Address
Phone (W) (H)	Phone (W) (H)
Name	Name
Address	Address
Phone (W) (H)	Phone (W) (H)
Name	Name
Address	Address
Phone (W) (H)	Phone (W) (H)

V - W - X

NAMES & ADDRESSES

Name

Address

Phone   (W)
          (H)

Name

Address

Phone   (W)
          (H)

Name

Address

Phone   (W)
          (H)

Name

Address

Phone   (W)
          (H)

Name

Address

Phone   (W)
          (H)

Name

Address

Phone   (W)
          (H)

Name

Address

Phone   (W)
          (H)

Name

Address

Phone   (W)
          (H)

Name

Address

Phone   (W)
          (H)

Name

Address

Phone   (W)
          (H)

Name

Address

Phone   (W)
          (H)

Name

Address

Phone   (W)
          (H)

Name

Address

Phone   (W)
          (H)

Name

Address

Phone   (W)
          (H)

Name

Address

Phone   (W)
          (H)

Name

Address

Phone   (W)
          (H)

Name

Address

Phone   (W)
          (H)

Name

Address

Phone   (W)
          (H)

Name

Address

Phone   (W)
          (H)

Name

Address

Phone   (W)
          (H)

Y - Z

CRISIS SCRIPTURE GUIDE

Alcohol & Substance Abuse - I Corinthians 6:19-20...Daniel 1:8...
Proverbs 20:1

Anger - Ephesians 4:26...Proverbs 16:32...Ephesians 4:31-32

Children - Exodus 20:12...Proverbs 22:6...Proverbs 23:13...Ephesians 6:1

Confusion - I Corinthians 14:33...Isaiah 50:7...James 3: 16-18

Danger - Psalm 91...I Peter 5:6-7...Psalm 46:1

Death - Isaiah 25:8...Revelation 21:4...Romans 14:8...Psalm 115:16

Decision-Making - Psalm 25:12...Proverbs 3:5-6...Proverbs 11:14

Depression - Psalm 37:4-5...Philippians 4:8...I Thessalonians 5:18

Despair - II Corinthians 4:8-9...Galatians 6:9...Psalm 27:14

Discouragement - Psalm 138:7...Hebrews 10:35-36...Psalm 31:24

Divorce - Matthew 5:31-32...Luke 1:18...Mark 10:2-12

Exhaustion - Isaiah 40:29-31...Psalm 55:22...Psalm 121:5-8

Failure - Romans 8:28...I Timothy 6:10-11...II Corinthians 4:8-9

Fear - Isaiah 41:10...I John 4:18...John 14:27

Financial Trouble - Philippians 4:19...Matthew 6:31-33...
II Corinthians 9:6-8

Grief - Psalm 23...II Corinthians 1:3-4...Revelation 21:4

Illness - Proverbs 4:20-22...James 5:14-15...III John 2

Isolation - Romans 8:38-39...Romans 8:35-39...Philippians 4:4

Loneliness - John 14:1-3...John 14:18...I Samuel 12:22

Lust - Galatians 5:16-17...James 1:14-15...II Timothy 2:22

Marriage - Genesis 2:18...Genesis 2:24...Proverbs 18:22

Old Age - Titus 2:2-4...Psalm 73:26...Psalm 90:10...Psalm 90:12

Rebellion - Isaiah 1:19-20...I Peter 5:5-6...Romans 6:12-13

Rejection - Psalm 27:10...Deuteromony 31:6...Psalm 147:3

Salvation - John 3:16...Romans 2:23...Romans 6:23...
Romans 10:9-10...Romans 10:13

Stress - Isaiah 30:18...Matthew 11:28-30...Psalm 107:5-7

Suffering - John 9:1-3...I Peter 4:12-13...I Peter 2:20-21

Temptation - I Corinthians 10:12-13...Hebrews 2:18...James 1:12-13

Trials - I Peter 4:12-13...Psalm 34:17-19...Psalm 56:11-13

Uncertainty - Psalm 37:4-5...Philippians 1:6...Psalm 23

Weakness - II Corinthians 12:8-10...Philippians 4:13...I Timothy 1:7

Worry - Philippians 4:5-6...Matthew 6:25-34...Philippians 4:8

Notes For Next Year

January

February

March

April

Notes For Next Year

May

_____

_____

_____

_____

_____

_____

_____

June

_____

_____

_____

_____

_____

_____

_____

July

_____

_____

_____

_____

_____

_____

August

_____

_____

_____

_____

_____

_____

NOTES FOR NEXT YEAR

September

October

November

December

NOTES

Notes

NOTES

NOTES

NOTES

NOTES